a b c d e f
g h i j k l
m n o p q r s
t u v w x y z

addressbook

a b c d e f
g h i j k l
m n o p q r s
t u v w x y z

RYLAND
PETERS
& SMALL
LONDON NEW YORK

paperstyle

Copyright © Ryland Peters & Small 2003.
Images taken from *Easy Flowers*
by Jane Durbridge and Antonia Swinson.
Photography by Polly Wreford,
copyright © Ryland Peters & Small 2003.
Published by Ryland Peters & Small
Kirkman House, 12–14 Whitfield Street, London W1T 2RP
519 Broadway, 5th Floor, New York NY 10012
www.rylandpeters.com

Isabel

a

name

address

phone

mobile

fax

e-mail

name

address

phone

mobile

fax

e-mail

name

address

phone

mobile

fax

e-mail

name

address

phone

mobile

fax

e-mail

name

address

phone

mobile

fax

e-mail

name

address

phone

mobile

fax

e-mail

name	
address	
phone	
mobile	
fax	
e-mail	

name	
address	
phone	
mobile	
fax	
e-mail	

name	
address	
phone	
mobile	
fax	
e-mail	

name

address

phone

mobile

fax

e-mail

name

address

phone

mobile

fax

e-mail

name

address

phone

mobile

fax

e-mail

name

address

phone

mobile

fax

e-mail

name

address

phone

mobile

fax

e-mail

name

address

phone

mobile

fax

e-mail

name

address

phone

mobile

fax

e-mail

name

address

phone

mobile

fax

e-mail

name

address

phone

mobile

fax

e-mail

name

address

phone

mobile

fax

e-mail

name

address

phone

mobile

fax

e-mail

name

address

phone

mobile

fax

e-mail

name

address

phone

mobile

fax

e-mail

name

address

phone

mobile

fax

e-mail

name

address

phone

mobile

fax

e-mail

name

address

phone

mobile

fax

e-mail

name

address

phone

mobile

fax

e-mail

name

address

phone

mobile

fax

e-mail

name

address

phone

mobile

fax

e-mail

name

address

phone

mobile

fax

e-mail

name

address

phone

mobile

fax

e-mail

name

address

phone

mobile

fax

e-mail

name

address

phone

mobile

fax

e-mail

name

address

phone

mobile

fax

e-mail

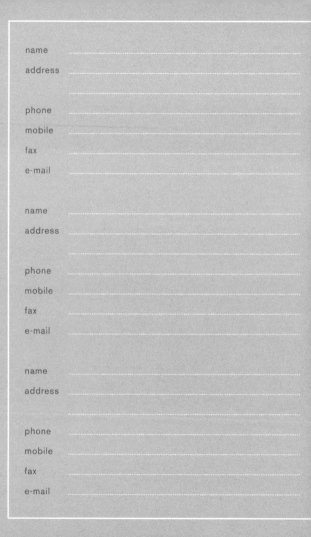

name

address

phone

mobile

fax

e-mail

name

address

phone

mobile

fax

e-mail

name

address

phone

mobile

fax

e-mail

name

address

phone

mobile

fax

e-mail

name

address

phone

mobile

fax

e-mail

name

address

phone

mobile

fax

e-mail

name

address

phone

mobile

fax

e-mail

name

address

phone

mobile

fax

e-mail

name

address

phone

mobile

fax

e-mail

name

address

phone

mobile

fax

e-mail

name

address

phone

mobile

fax

e-mail

name

address

phone

mobile

fax

e-mail

name	
address	
phone	
mobile	
fax	
e-mail	
name	
address	
phone	
mobile	
fax	
e-mail	
name	
address	
phone	
mobile	
fax	
e-mail	

C

name

address

phone

mobile

fax

e-mail

name

address

phone

mobile

fax

e-mail

name

address

phone

mobile

fax

e-mail

name

address

phone

mobile

fax

e-mail

name

address

phone

mobile

fax

e-mail

name

address

phone

mobile

fax

e-mail

name

address

phone

mobile

fax

e-mail

name

address

phone

mobile

fax

e-mail

name

address

phone

mobile

fax

e-mail

name

address

phone

mobile

fax

e-mail

name

address

phone

mobile

fax

e-mail

name

address

phone

mobile

fax

e-mail

name

address

phone

mobile

fax

e-mail

name

address

phone

mobile

fax

e-mail

name

address

phone

mobile

fax

e-mail

name	
address	
phone	
mobile	
fax	
e-mail	

name	
address	
phone	
mobile	
fax	
e-mail	

name	
address	
phone	
mobile	
fax	
e-mail	

name

address

phone

mobile

fax

e-mail

name

address

phone

mobile

fax

e-mail

name

address

phone

mobile

fax

e-mail

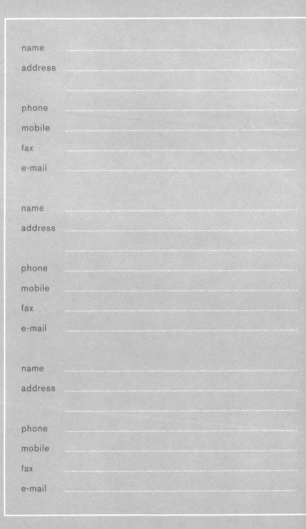

name

address

phone

mobile

fax

e-mail

name

address

phone

mobile

fax

e-mail

name

address

phone

mobile

fax

e-mail

name

address

phone

mobile

fax

e-mail

name

address

phone

mobile

fax

e-mail

name

address

phone

mobile

fax

e-mail

name	
address	
phone	
mobile	
fax	
e-mail	
name	
address	
phone	
mobile	
fax	
e-mail	
name	
address	
phone	
mobile	
fax	
e-mail	

name

address

phone

mobile

fax

e-mail

name

address

phone

mobile

fax

e-mail

name

address

phone

mobile

fax

e-mail

name	
address	
phone	
mobile	
fax	
e-mail	
name	
address	
phone	
mobile	
fax	
e-mail	
name	
address	
phone	
mobile	
fax	
e-mail	

name

address

phone

mobile

fax

e-mail

name

address

phone

mobile

fax

e-mail

name

address

phone

mobile

fax

e-mail

name

address

phone

mobile

fax

e-mail

name

address

phone

mobile

fax

e-mail

name

address

phone

mobile

fax

e-mail

name ....

address ....

....

phone ....

mobile ....

fax ....

e-mail ....

name ....

address ....

....

phone ....

mobile ....

fax ....

e-mail ....

name ....

address ....

....

phone ....

mobile ....

fax ....

e-mail ....

name

address

phone

mobile

fax

e-mail

name

address

phone

mobile

fax

e-mail

name

address

phone

mobile

fax

e-mail

name

address

phone

mobile

fax

e-mail

name

address

phone

mobile

fax

e-mail

name

address

phone

mobile

fax

e-mail

name

address

phone

mobile

fax

e-mail

name

address

phone

mobile

fax

e-mail

name

address

phone

mobile

fax

e-mail

name

address

phone

mobile

fax

e-mail

name

address

phone

mobile

fax

e-mail

name

address

phone

mobile

fax

e-mail

name	
address	
phone	
mobile	
fax	
e-mail	
name	
address	
phone	
mobile	
fax	
e-mail	
name	
address	
phone	
mobile	
fax	
e-mail	

name

address

phone

mobile

fax

e-mail

name

address

phone

mobile

fax

e-mail

name

address

phone

mobile

fax

e-mail

name

address

phone

mobile

fax

e-mail

name

address

phone

mobile

fax

e-mail

name

address

phone

mobile

fax

e-mail

name

address

phone

mobile

fax

e-mail

name

address

phone

mobile

fax

e-mail

name

address

phone

mobile

fax

e-mail

name

address

phone

mobile

fax

e-mail

name

address

phone

mobile

fax

e-mail

name

address

phone

mobile

fax

e-mail

f

name

address

phone

mobile

fax

e-mail

name

address

phone

mobile

fax

e-mail

name

address

phone

mobile

fax

e-mail

name

address

phone

mobile

fax

e-mail

name

address

phone

mobile

fax

e-mail

name

address

phone

mobile

fax

e-mail

name

address

phone

mobile

fax

e-mail

name

address

phone

mobile

fax

e-mail

name

address

phone

mobile

fax

e-mail

name

address

phone

mobile

fax

e-mail

name

address

phone

mobile

fax

e-mail

name

address

phone

mobile

fax

e-mail

name

address

phone

mobile

fax

e-mail

name

address

phone

mobile

fax

e-mail

name

address

phone

mobile

fax

e-mail

name	
address	
phone	
mobile	
fax	
e-mail	
name	
address	
phone	
mobile	
fax	
e-mail	
name	
address	
phone	
mobile	
fax	
e-mail	

name

address

phone

mobile

fax

e-mail

name

address

phone

mobile

fax

e-mail

name

address

phone

mobile

fax

e-mail

name

address

phone

mobile

fax

e-mail

name

address

phone

mobile

fax

e-mail

name

address

phone

mobile

fax

e-mail

name

address

phone

mobile

fax

e-mail

name

address

phone

mobile

fax

e-mail

name

address

phone

mobile

fax

e-mail

name

address

phone

mobile

fax

e-mail

name

address

phone

mobile

fax

e-mail

name

address

phone

mobile

fax

e-mail

name

address

phone

mobile

fax

e-mail

name

address

phone

mobile

fax

e-mail

name

address

phone

mobile

fax

e-mail

name

address

phone

mobile

fax

e-mail

name

address

phone

mobile

fax

e-mail

name

address

phone

mobile

fax

e-mail

name

address

phone

mobile

fax

e-mail

name

address

phone

mobile

fax

e-mail

name

address

phone

mobile

fax

e-mail

name

address

phone

mobile

fax

e-mail

name

address

phone

mobile

fax

e-mail

name

address

phone

mobile

fax

e-mail

name

address

phone

mobile

fax

e-mail

name

address

phone

mobile

fax

e-mail

name

address

phone

mobile

fax

e-mail

name

address

phone

mobile

fax

e-mail

name

address

phone

mobile

fax

e-mail

name

address

phone

mobile

fax

e-mail

h

name	
address	
phone	
mobile	
fax	
e-mail	
name	
address	
phone	
mobile	
fax	
e-mail	
name	
address	
phone	
mobile	
fax	
e-mail	

name

address

phone

mobile

fax

e-mail

name

address

phone

mobile

fax

e-mail

name

address

phone

mobile

fax

e-mail

name

address

phone

mobile

fax

e-mail

name

address

phone

mobile

fax

e-mail

name

address

phone

mobile

fax

e-mail

name

address

phone

mobile

fax

e-mail

name

address

phone

mobile

fax

e-mail

name

address

phone

mobile

fax

e-mail

name

address

phone

mobile

fax

e-mail

name

address

phone

mobile

fax

e-mail

name

address

phone

mobile

fax

e-mail

name

address

phone

mobile

fax

e-mail

name

address

phone

mobile

fax

e-mail

name

address

phone

mobile

fax

e-mail

name

address

phone

mobile

fax

e-mail

name

address

phone

mobile

fax

e-mail

name

address

phone

mobile

fax

e-mail

name

address

phone

mobile

fax

e-mail

name

address

phone

mobile

fax

e-mail

name

address

phone

mobile

fax

e-mail

name

address

phone

mobile

fax

e-mail

name

address

phone

mobile

fax

e-mail

name

address

phone

mobile

fax

e-mail

name

address

phone

mobile

fax

e-mail

name

address

phone

mobile

fax

e-mail

name

address

phone

mobile

fax

e-mail

name

address

phone

mobile

fax

e-mail

name

address

phone

mobile

fax

e-mail

name

address

phone

mobile

fax

e-mail

name

address

phone

mobile

fax

e-mail

name

address

phone

mobile

fax

e-mail

name

address

phone

mobile

fax

e-mail

name

address

phone

mobile

fax

e-mail

name

address

phone

mobile

fax

e-mail

name

address

phone

mobile

fax

e-mail

name

address

phone

mobile

fax

e-mail

name

address

phone

mobile

fax

e-mail

name

address

phone

mobile

fax

e-mail

name	
address	
phone	
mobile	
fax	
e-mail	
name	
address	
phone	
mobile	
fax	
e-mail	
name	
address	
phone	
mobile	
fax	
e-mail	

name

address

phone

mobile

fax

e-mail

name

address

phone

mobile

fax

e-mail

name

address

phone

mobile

fax

e-mail

name

address

phone

mobile

fax

e-mail

name

address

phone

mobile

fax

e-mail

name

address

phone

mobile

fax

e-mail

name	
address	
phone	
mobile	
fax	
e-mail	

name	
address	
phone	
mobile	
fax	
e-mail	

name	
address	
phone	
mobile	
fax	
e-mail	

name

address

phone

mobile

fax

e-mail

name

address

phone

mobile

fax

e-mail

name

address

phone

mobile

fax

e-mail

name

address

phone

mobile

fax

e-mail

name

address

phone

mobile

fax

e-mail

name

address

phone

mobile

fax

e-mail

name

address

phone

mobile

fax

e-mail

name

address

phone

mobile

fax

e-mail

name

address

phone

mobile

fax

e-mail

name

address

phone

mobile

fax

e-mail

name

address

phone

mobile

fax

e-mail

name

address

phone

mobile

fax

e-mail

name

address

phone

mobile

fax

e-mail

name

address

phone

mobile

fax

e-mail

name

address

phone

mobile

fax

e-mail

name

address

phone

mobile

fax

e-mail

name

address

phone

mobile

fax

e-mail

name

address

phone

mobile

fax

e-mail

name

address

phone

mobile

fax

e-mail

name

address

phone

mobile

fax

e-mail

name

address

phone

mobile

fax

e-mail

name

address

phone

mobile

fax

e-mail

name

address

phone

mobile

fax

e-mail

name

address

phone

mobile

fax

e-mail

name

address

phone

mobile

fax

e-mail

name

address

phone

mobile

fax

e-mail

name

address

phone

mobile

fax

e-mail

name

address

phone

mobile

fax

e-mail

name

address

phone

mobile

fax

e-mail

name

address

phone

mobile

fax

e-mail

name

address

phone

mobile

fax

e-mail

name

address

phone

mobile

fax

e-mail

name

address

phone

mobile

fax

e-mail

name

address

phone

mobile

fax

e-mail

name

address

phone

mobile

fax

e-mail

name

address

phone

mobile

fax

e-mail

name

address

phone

mobile

fax

e-mail

name

address

phone

mobile

fax

e-mail

name

address

phone

mobile

fax

e-mail

name

address

phone

mobile

fax

e-mail

name

address

phone

mobile

fax

e-mail

name

address

phone

mobile

fax

e-mail

n

name

address

phone

mobile

fax

e-mail

name

address

phone

mobile

fax

e-mail

name

address

phone

mobile

fax

e-mail

name

address

phone

mobile

fax

e-mail

name

address

phone

mobile

fax

e-mail

name

address

phone

mobile

fax

e-mail

name

address

phone

mobile

fax

e-mail

name

address

phone

mobile

fax

e-mail

name

address

phone

mobile

fax

e-mail

name

address

phone

mobile

fax

e-mail

name

address

phone

mobile

fax

e-mail

name

address

phone

mobile

fax

e-mail

name

address

phone

mobile

fax

e-mail

name

address

phone

mobile

fax

e-mail

name

address

phone

mobile

fax

e-mail

name

address

phone

mobile

fax

e-mail

name

address

phone

mobile

fax

e-mail

name

address

phone

mobile

fax

e-mail

name

address

phone

mobile

fax

e-mail

name

address

phone

mobile

fax

e-mail

name

address

phone

mobile

fax

e-mail

name

address

phone

mobile

fax

e-mail

name

address

phone

mobile

fax

e-mail

name

address

phone

mobile

fax

e-mail

name

address

phone

mobile

fax

e-mail

name

address

phone

mobile

fax

e-mail

name

address

phone

mobile

fax

e-mail

name

address

phone

mobile

fax

e-mail

name

address

phone

mobile

fax

e-mail

name

address

phone

mobile

fax

e-mail

name

address

phone

mobile

fax

e-mail

name

address

phone

mobile

fax

e-mail

name

address

phone

mobile

fax

e-mail

name

address

phone

mobile

fax

e-mail

name

address

phone

mobile

fax

e-mail

name

address

phone

mobile

fax

e-mail

name

address

phone

mobile

fax

e-mail

name

address

phone

mobile

fax

e-mail

name

address

phone

mobile

fax

e-mail

name

address

phone

mobile

fax

e-mail

name

address

phone

mobile

fax

e-mail

name

address

phone

mobile

fax

e-mail

name

address

phone

mobile

fax

e-mail

name

address

phone

mobile

fax

e-mail

name

address

phone

mobile

fax

e-mail

name

address

phone

mobile

fax

e-mail

name

address

phone

mobile

fax

e-mail

name

address

phone

mobile

fax

e-mail

name

address

phone

mobile

fax

e-mail

name

address

phone

mobile

fax

e-mail

name

address

phone

mobile

fax

e-mail

name ....

address ....

....

phone ....

mobile ....

fax ....

e-mail ....

name ....

address ....

....

phone ....

mobile ....

fax ....

e-mail ....

name ....

address ....

....

phone ....

mobile ....

fax ....

e-mail ....

name

address

phone

mobile

fax

e-mail

name

address

phone

mobile

fax

e-mail

name

address

phone

mobile

fax

e-mail

name

address

phone

mobile

fax

e-mail

name

address

phone

mobile

fax

e-mail

name

address

phone

mobile

fax

e-mail

name

address

phone

mobile

fax

e-mail

name

address

phone

mobile

fax

e-mail

name

address

phone

mobile

fax

e-mail

name

address

phone

mobile

fax

e-mail

name

address

phone

mobile

fax

e-mail

name

address

phone

mobile

fax

e-mail

r

name

address

phone

mobile

fax

e-mail

name

address

phone

mobile

fax

e-mail

name

address

phone

mobile

fax

e-mail

name

address

phone

mobile

fax

e-mail

name

address

phone

mobile

fax

e-mail

name

address

phone

mobile

fax

e-mail

name

address

phone

mobile

fax

e-mail

name

address

phone

mobile

fax

e-mail

name

address

phone

mobile

fax

e-mail

name

address

phone

mobile

fax

e-mail

name

address

phone

mobile

fax

e-mail

name

address

phone

mobile

fax

e-mail

name

address

phone

mobile

fax

e-mail

name

address

phone

mobile

fax

e-mail

name

address

phone

mobile

fax

e-mail

name

address

phone

mobile

fax

e-mail

name

address

phone

mobile

fax

e-mail

name

address

phone

mobile

fax

e-mail

name

address

phone

mobile

fax

e-mail

name

address

phone

mobile

fax

e-mail

name

address

phone

mobile

fax

e-mail

name

address

phone

mobile

fax

e-mail

name

address

phone

mobile

fax

e-mail

name

address

phone

mobile

fax

e-mail

S

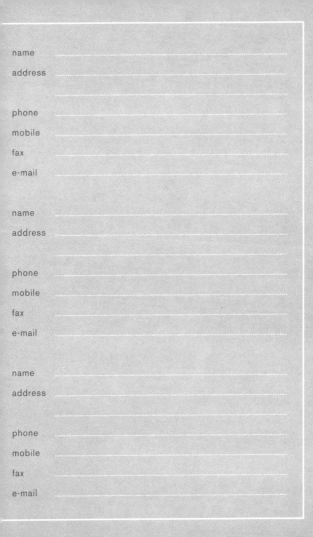

name

address

phone

mobile

fax

e-mail

name

address

phone

mobile

fax

e-mail

name

address

phone

mobile

fax

e-mail

name	
address	
phone	
mobile	
fax	
e-mail	

name	
address	
phone	
mobile	
fax	
e-mail	

name	
address	
phone	
mobile	
fax	
e-mail	

name	
address	
phone	
mobile	
fax	
e-mail	

name	
address	
phone	
mobile	
fax	
e-mail	

name	
address	
phone	
mobile	
fax	
e-mail	

name

address

phone

mobile

fax

e-mail

name

address

phone

mobile

fax

e-mail

name

address

phone

mobile

fax

e-mail

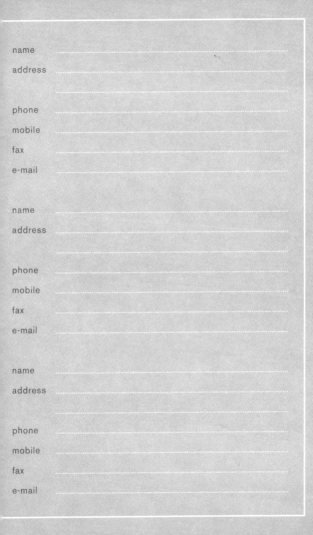

name

address

phone

mobile

fax

e-mail

name

address

phone

mobile

fax

e-mail

name

address

phone

mobile

fax

e-mail

name

address

phone

mobile

fax

e-mail

name

address

phone

mobile

fax

e-mail

name

address

phone

mobile

fax

e-mail

name

address

phone

mobile

fax

e-mail

name

address

phone

mobile

fax

e-mail

name

address

phone

mobile

fax

e-mail

name

address

phone

mobile

fax

e-mail

name

address

phone

mobile

fax

e-mail

name

address

phone

mobile

fax

e-mail

t

name

address

phone

mobile

fax

e-mail

name

address

phone

mobile

fax

e-mail

name

address

phone

mobile

fax

e-mail

name

address

phone

mobile

fax

e-mail

name

address

phone

mobile

fax

e-mail

name

address

phone

mobile

fax

e-mail

name

address

phone

mobile

fax

e-mail

name

address

phone

mobile

fax

e-mail

name

address

phone

mobile

fax

e-mail

name

address

phone

mobile

fax

e-mail

name

address

phone

mobile

fax

e-mail

name

address

phone

mobile

fax

e-mail

name

address

phone

mobile

fax

e-mail

name

address

phone

mobile

fax

e-mail

name

address

phone

mobile

fax

e-mail

name

address

phone

mobile

fax

e-mail

name

address

phone

mobile

fax

e-mail

name

address

phone

mobile

fax

e-mail

name

address

phone

mobile

fax

e-mail

name

address

phone

mobile

fax

e-mail

name

address

phone

mobile

fax

e-mail

name

address

phone

mobile

fax

e-mail

name

address

phone

mobile

fax

e-mail

name

address

phone

mobile

fax

e-mail

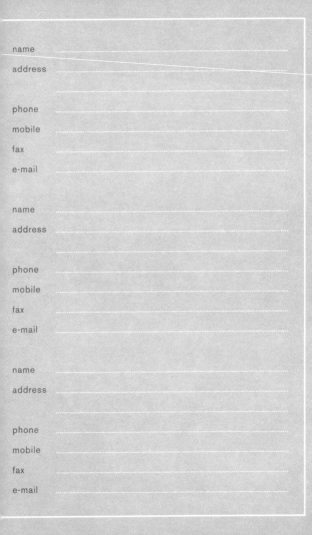

name
address

phone
mobile
fax
e-mail

name
address

phone
mobile
fax
e-mail

name
address

phone
mobile
fax
e-mail

name

address

phone

mobile

fax

e-mail

name

address

phone

mobile

fax

e-mail

name

address

phone

mobile

fax

e-mail

name

address

phone

mobile

fax

e-mail

name

address

phone

mobile

fax

e-mail

name

address

phone

mobile

fax

e-mail

name

address

phone

mobile

fax

e-mail

name

address

phone

mobile

fax

e-mail

name

address

phone

mobile

fax

e-mail

name

address

phone

mobile

fax

e-mail

name

address

phone

mobile

fax

e-mail

name

address

phone

mobile

fax

e-mail

name

address

phone

mobile

fax

e-mail

name

address

phone

mobile

fax

e-mail

name

address

phone

mobile

fax

e-mail

name

address

phone

mobile

fax

e-mail

name

address

phone

mobile

fax

e-mail

name

address

phone

mobile

fax

e-mail

name

address

phone

mobile

fax

e-mail

name

address

phone

mobile

fax

e-mail

name

address

phone

mobile

fax

e-mail

name

address

phone

mobile

fax

e-mail

name

address

phone

mobile

fax

e-mail

name

address

phone

mobile

fax

e-mail

name

address

phone

mobile

fax

e-mail

name

address

phone

mobile

fax

e-mail

name

address

phone

mobile

fax

e-mail

name

address

phone

mobile

fax

e-mail

name

address

phone

mobile

fax

e-mail

name

address

phone

mobile

fax

e-mail

name	
address	
phone	
mobile	
fax	
e-mail	
name	
address	
phone	
mobile	
fax	
e-mail	
name	
address	
phone	
mobile	
fax	
e-mail	

yz

name	
address	
phone	
mobile	
fax	
e-mail	

name	
address	
phone	
mobile	
fax	
e-mail	

name	
address	
phone	
mobile	
fax	
e-mail	

name

address

phone

mobile

fax

e-mail

name

address

phone

mobile

fax

e-mail

name

address

phone

mobile

fax

e-mail

name

address

phone

mobile

fax

e-mail

name

address

phone

mobile

fax

e-mail

name

address

phone

mobile

fax

e-mail

name

address

phone

mobile

fax

e-mail

name

address

phone

mobile

fax

e-mail

name

address

phone

mobile

fax

e-mail

name

address

phone

mobile

fax

e-mail

name

address

phone

mobile

fax

e-mail

name

address

phone

mobile

fax

e-mail

name

address

phone

mobile

fax

e-mail

name

address

phone

mobile

fax

e-mail

name

address

phone

mobile

fax

e-mail